# Peter's Railway
## A Dark & Stormy Night

**by**
## Christopher Vine

The watercolour illustrations are by John Wardle

Published by
Christopher Vine 2011

Printed by The Amadeus Press
Copyright © 2011 Christopher Vine

ISBN 978-0-9553359-8-3

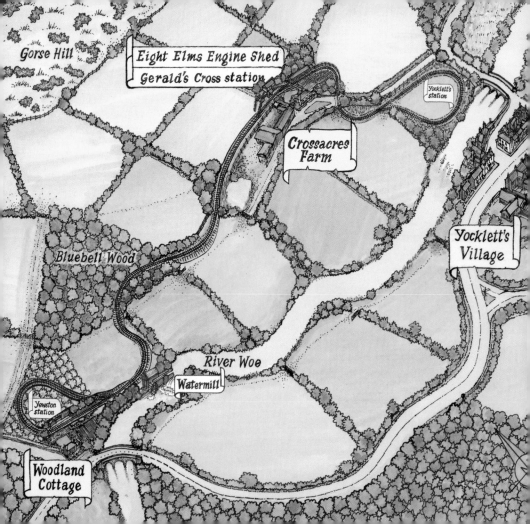

# The Peter's Railway Series

Peter and his Grandpa have built an amazing miniature steam railway between their houses; Woodland Cottage and Crossacres Farm. The line even runs to Yockletts Village where Peter goes to school.

The locomotive, Fiery Fox, is a wonderful machine. Bright green and very powerful, it can pull heavy trains along the line at high speed. They have even banked up the track on the bends so the trains can run really fast.

After a mishap while doing some track maintenance, Grandpa remembers one of his amazing-but-true stories from an old railway.

# A Dark and Stormy Night

It had been a busy summer on Peter's Railway. With lots of visitors, trains had been running almost every day.

Fiery Fox, the powerful locomotive was still as good as new. There was not a single rattle or squeak from any part of her fascinating mechanism. Everything moved with the grace and elegance of a beautiful animal.

Unfortunately the same could not be said for the track. With all the heavy trains and the freezing winter, the line was getting a little bumpy in places. When Fiery Fox was running fast, the passengers were getting shaken up.

It was time to do some track maintenance.

"We will need several truckloads of ballast stones to put under the sleepers," said Grandpa to Peter. "We'll also need a shovel, and a spirit level to check that the track is really flat."

With the wagons loaded up, they pushed them down the line to the first of the rough bits and set to work.

Grandpa lifted the track a little, while Peter shovelled some fresh ballast underneath. After a bit of adjusting, they checked it with the spirit level. Perfect!

The next bad spot was at the top of the field by the river. The line sloped downhill here so they put a small stick on one of the rails to stop the wagons from rolling off down the hill.

With the wagons a few metres behind them, Grandpa lifted the track.

"I'll need to put some ballast under here," said Peter, looking underneath. But when he turned round to get it, the trucks were nowhere to be seen.

"They must have rolled off down the hill while we were looking the other way!" laughed Grandpa. "That stick wasn't big enough. We'd better give chase and hope they haven't come off the track at the bend by the river."

"Like Grandma nearly did...." added Peter, remembering a day of near disaster. Grandma had not been amused.

"Don't remind me!" groaned Grandpa, and they set off in hot pursuit.

When they finally caught up with the train at the curve by the river, they found a scene of destruction. Ballast, tools and trucks were scattered all over the place. It was a terrible mess.

Luckily the wagons hadn't been damaged in the crash as they had landed on some soft grass. So Peter and Grandpa set about putting them back on the rails and clearing up the spilt ballast.

Then they sat down for a while to watch the river. "Our accident just now," said Grandpa, "has reminded me of a true story. Have I ever told you about the amazing train crash at Sandgate station?"

"No you haven't," replied Peter, who enjoyed a good train crash story. "I'd love to hear it!"

"First of all I must set the scene," began Grandpa, "and explain about the branch line down to Hythe and Sandgate; two small towns by the sea in Kent.

"For years," he continued, "the two towns didn't have a railway, because they were too far from the main line which ran from London to Folkestone and Dover. There was also the added problem that they were quite a bit downhill from the existing line.

"Eventually though, a short branch was built. It ran down quite a steep hill or gradient, first to Hythe and then on to the end, or terminus station at Sandgate.

"It was never a busy line but there was a small goods yard at Hythe.

"Usually freight trains would be made up in the yard. But at Hythe it was so small that they used the running line through the station when there were no passenger trains.

"Because the railway was on a gradient, they would first put one or two guard's vans on the line, with their brakes wound tightly on. They acted as buffers to stop the wagons rolling down the hill towards Sandgate.

"Then it was simply a case of shoving, or loose shunting, the wagons off down the track, until they bumped into the guard's vans. When they were all in a row, the men would couple them together, ready to be hauled up to London.

"Before I get to the night of the disaster," Grandpa added, "I must tell you about 'catch' points on a railway."

He explained that catch points are a safety feature which divert runaway wagons away from danger and prevent crashes. Usually the catch points just derail them off to one side of the track, where they can't do any damage. They are set from the signal box.

"At Sandgate," Grandpa continued, "the catch points were just outside the station. They prevented any runaway wagons from crashing into a passenger train, waiting at the platform. There was a bit of spare land beside the track, the perfect place to ditch speeding trucks, out of harm's way.

"The 14th June, 1929, was a dark and stormy night!" Grandpa spoke dramatically. "A goods train was being marshalled at Hythe Station.

"As usual, the men had put two guard's vans on the running line and had firmly applied the brakes while they sorted out the rest of the wagons.

"They were working in the dark.

"When they shunted the first wagon down onto the guard's vans, they didn't hear the familiar metallic clang, as the buffers met. They assumed that this was because the wind was blowing so hard that the sound had been blown away and they simply had not heard it.

"But in fact the guard's vans had rolled off down the hill.......

"Of course there shouldn't have been any danger," continued Grandpa. "Because the catch points would derail any runaways at Sandgate.

"Unfortunately though, two nice bungalow houses had recently been built on the piece of scrap land, just beside the catch points! They were called Belle Vue and Holcombe.

"The first the residents knew of their impending doom was a loud rumbling in the night.

"Before they could do anything, two guard's vans came crashing through the fence, demolishing one corner of Belle Vue!

"Then moments later, a wagon-load of ash hurtled off the track and wrecked the bathroom of Holcombe!"

"What happened to the people in the houses?" asked Peter quickly.

"They had a very lucky escape!" replied Grandpa. "They just happened to be in different rooms at the time of the crash."

"And what did the shunters at Hythe do about it?" Peter wanted to know.

"That's the best part," chuckled Grandpa, enjoying his story. "They didn't know anything was wrong and just kept shunting wagons into the night.

"They thought they were making up the train, when in fact they were just sending more trucks down the line to crash into the houses!

"The first the shunters knew of their spectacular mistake was when they went to couple all the wagons together. The whole lot had disappeared!

"Of course the householders made quite a fuss and the Southern Railway agreed to pay them £175 in damages. A lot of money in 1929.

"And as you can imagine, the men involved got into a whole load of trouble for being so careless.

"To stop the same thing happening again, the railway company moved the catch points to somewhere much safer."

"And what happened to the two houses?" asked Peter.

"After all the wreckage had been cleared away," replied Grandpa, "the houses were completely repaired and things returned to normal: A sleepy branch line.

"Sadly, if you go there today, the railway has gone. It was scrapped many years ago and houses have been built all over the track bed and station."

"Next time we visit the Romney Hythe and Dymchurch Railway," suggested Peter as they got back to work on their own railway, "perhaps we could do a small detour to Sandgate and see if we can find Belle Vue and Holcombe.

"I wonder if the people who live there today have any idea what happened to their houses, a long time ago, on a dark and stormy night....?"

The End.

# Why Peter's Railway?

Since a very small boy, Chris has always loved anything mechanical and especially steam engines. The first workshop was in his bedroom where he made an electric go-kart aged 8, followed by a mini-bike powered by the engine from a petrol lawn mower.

He spent many holidays on a friend's farm where there was a miniature railway across a field and so started a love of making model steam locomotives. The latest is Bongo, 8 feet long and the inspiration for Fiery Fox in the books.

Chris wanted to share his love and knowledge of railways and engineering:  Peter's Railway is the result.

**Story**        **Technical**        **Adventure**

# The original books

The original four books tell the charming story of Peter and his Grandpa building and running their steam railway across the farm. At the ends of chapters are special how-it-works pages with simple (but accurate) explanations of what has been happening in the story. In addition, Grandpa tells some wonderful stories from the old days on the railways.     Age range 6 - 12 years approx.

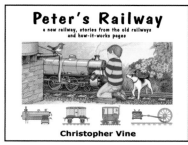

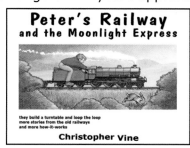

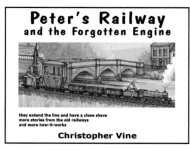

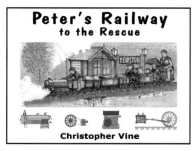

Hardback, 96 pages 17 x 24 cm with 30 watercolour pictures by John Wardle and 14 pages of clearly explained technical drawings.  £11.99

# New!  Small format books

A new series of Peter's Railway in a smaller format. While the original books each contain several story or adventure threads, separate technical pages and Grandpa's tales, the small books concentrate on one aspect; a Peter's adventure, a Grandpa's tale of the old railways or a technical book.

'Little Peter's Railway' are gentle stories for younger children.

**Little
Peter's Railway
Christmas Steam**
Peter saves Christmas

**Little
Peter's Railway
Surprise Goods**
A bed-time story with a twist....

**Peter's Railway
A Bit of Energy**
Grandpa tries to answer a tricky question

**Peter's Railway
A Dark and Stormy Night**
Grandpa tells a tale from the old days

Paperbacks with 32 pages, 12 watercolour pictures - £2.99